"ONLY CONNECT"

A BOOK OF STORIES

ERWIN C. HARGROVE

ISBN 978-1-7325395-7-0 paperback
     978-1-7325395-8-7 epub
     978-1-7325395-9-4 mobi

Preface

EM Forster wrote in *Howards End* about two families that were very different. One family lived for the outer world and the other family cultivated the inner life. The book is about their efforts to combine the two approaches to life. Forster summed this up with a phrase that has been quoted over and over.

"Only connect the prose and the passion."

This book of stories is about people who are trying to connect prose and passion in the latter parts of their lives.

Table of Contents

Chapter 1

"Only Connect"

Andy loved his wife but did not like her family. Her Father and two brothers owned a company that manufactured wire rope. Business was their life. He taught English at a small college and wrote novels. His wife, Beth, did not seem to belong in her family. She wrote poetry and acted in a small repertory company. Her family lived in Cleveland, and he and his wife lived in North Carolina. He dreaded the annual trip to Cleveland for Thanksgiving. Her family was strongly Republican, and he was a relaxed Democrat. He was always on the defensive. Why would anyone study English? You can't get a job that way. If he understood business he would not be a Democrat.

He published his first novel when he was thirty-five, and it was reviewed as promising. The next two novels came in the next ten years and were favorably reviewed. But he was not a major

American writer. His teaching and writing were a seamless web. He did not think that anyone in her family read the novels. They were never discussed.

Beth's family saw college as an extension of high school, something to get through before you went to work. They were engineers, and he knew nothing about engineering, except he noticed that they thought that all problems could be solved. There were few, in any, uncertainties.

Beth's mother and the two daughters-in-law were nice to him. They never joined in the dinner table discussions about politics or business. They deferred to their husbands. Beth tried to stick up for him, and once left the table crying when her father and brother all jumped on him for his opposition to the American war in Vietnam.

Andy and Beth had met on a ship going to Europe in their college years. He was at Davidson and she was at Sweet Briar. They decided to marry after a year of long distance courtship. He met her family not long before the wedding. Andy's father was a historian at the University of North Carolina and his mother was a poet. They came to the wedding but had very little in common with Beth's parents' friends. He felt the same way. His parents and grandparents were cultured people. The friends of Beth's parents seemed to have the one accomplishment of material success. Otherwise they were commonplace. Andy could not help but feel superior, even though he knew that he was not respected, because he was different.

Beth's father had created a wire rope company and made it successful in the boom after World War II. Chinese competition entered markets in the nineteen eighties and the free trade policies of Republican administrations were a threat to the firm. Her Father railed against the government in Washington, despite it being Republican. As a result, business began to slip. The company could not compete with prices that undercut his prices. He had to watch the company that he had founded decline, and he was helpless to prevent it. His two sons left to join other manufacturing firms, and eventually he had to declare bankruptcy. The old man had ruined his health by hard work, lack of exercise, cigarettes, and bourbon. His heart began to fail, and his wife had to put him in a retirement home, where he could be looked after. She went as well, and her life, which had been busy with luncheons, parties, and grandchildren, seemed to wither. They were in a custodial setting, which neither of them liked, but what were they to do?

One day in June Andy went to visit his father-in-law. Beth and her mother were shopping. The old man was sitting in his apartment staring out the window and barely seemed to notice when he walked in and sat down. Andy had no idea what they could talk about and, in desperation, came up with a question: "What did you like to do when you were a boy?"

The eyes in the old face suddenly brightened. The voice was stronger than usual. "I grew up in small town in Ohio. We boys had the country side at our doorstep. I loved to fish, first with a cane pole and then with a real spinning rod. Later my father taught me to hunt and to use a gun. We went hunting for quail. I still remember hearing 'Bob White' across the fields. We had wonderful dogs. My job was to look after them. They were friends more than pets. My friends and I all learned to hunt. I remember the excitement of sitting in the early morning just before the ducks flew over. And then they came. It was beautiful."

"What else did you do?"

"We boys went to the silent movies on Saturday afternoons. They were usually cowboy pictures. I still remember the piano tunes timed to action on the screen. In the summer, we swam in the river where there was a beach. I was a lifeguard in high school and college and was very proud of it. The girls would hang around the lifeguard station. It was wonderful."

Then the old man looked at him. "What did you do?"

Andy was stuck for a moment. It would not do to say that he read a lot of books. "I loved to play baseball," he said. "We played a game we called 'workup.' If a batter didn't get a base hit, he had to go to the outfield and gradually work up through bases until he could bat again. I was a pretty good hitter, so I got to bat a lot. Some boys could pitch well and could stay on the mound but get to bat if they gave up a hit.

"We went to the movies too," Andy continued, "especially Westerns. I especially liked Hopalong Cassidy. The Three Stooges made me laugh so hard I could hardly breathe. And then the horror movies, Bela Lugosi, that scared me to death. I loved high school. There was a dance hall outside town called the 'Frog Hop.' We took dates to dance to the 'big bands' that came to town, the Dorsey Brothers, Woody Herman, Stan Kenton. Life was fun."

The old man was listening. "Our lives weren't so different. How did you ever get to be a writer?"

"I was a reader, and writing was easy for me. I began to write stories in high school and was on a literary magazine at Davidson. A few of my stories were published, but I could not make a living writing. I got a degree in 'creative writing,' which permitted me to teach English. I just kept at it, and my first novel was published eventually after a lot of very hard work. The college wanted me all the more after that, so I just kept it up. I have published three novels now, and they have been well reviewed, but I love teaching. So I have the best of both worlds."

It was Andy's turn to ask a question. "How did you first get started in business?"

"I studied mechanical engineering. I was always interested in how machines worked. My first job was with a firm that made machinist equipment. That was where I learned about wire rope. I began to study how to make it, and eventually formed a small company with help from a Cleveland bank. The market for the product was expanding. I hired good engineers and trained workers for the necessary skills, and we just grew and grew. It was very exciting to build a new company, create jobs for people, and make money as a reward."

"I am sorry that that day has gone."

"Yes, but that's how business works. I have learned to accept that, slowly and painfully. But I had the excitement of creating something out of nothing and making it work for a long time. Isn't that what you do when you write a novel?"

Andy hadn't expected that question. "I suppose so. I combine my talent with my experience to create. That's what you did."

The old man smiled. "We did pretty much the same thing. I never thought of it that way."

They were quiet for a moment, and then Beth and her mother returned. Andy had to say goodbye, as they were going home. "I'll be back before long, Bert." He had never called him Bert or anything else for that matter. "Take care of yourself."

"So long, Andy. I have one of your novels, and I'm going to read it."

As they were walking to the car, he said to Beth a phrase she knew: "only connect."

Chapter 2

A CHANCE MEETING

Reid and Alice met at a dinner party at the home of friends.. It was a table of eight, and they were seated next to each other, he at the end and she beside him. The conversation at dinner was light across the table, but they managed to tell each other something about themselves. They were in their forties, married with children. He was a lawyer, and she taught handicapped children. They had talked a little over drinks before dinner, but he had not noticed anything special about her.

After dessert and coffee, the rest of the party moved into the living room and gathered around the piano to sing. The pianist knew endless numbers of popular songs, many from their younger days, and the guests had great fun, but for some reason the two of them stayed at the table.

He was not sure why, but he knew that he wanted to stay with her. Their conversation had drawn them together. They talked for at least an hour. The hostess came over several times to urge them to join the group, but they declined. His wife and her husband were at the piano, but Reid paid no attention, nor did Alice.

At one point, she told him that she liked him. She said it very softly and later said that she was not sure that he had heard her. He did hear her and gave a relaxed sigh. He did not know what was happening, but it was very good.

The party broke up and all went home. He did not mention her to his wife, nor did she ask him what they talked about or why he had stayed at the table. He had a secret he wanted to keep.

The next week, he called her and asked her for lunch. She did not hesitate. They met at an out-of-the-way restaurant. Nothing was said about what they were doing. They just enjoyed being together.

After that, they met for lunch about once a month. She kissed him on the cheek once. He never asked her about her marriage, but from what she said, he gathered that it was good. She and her husband had two children in college to whom she was devoted. It was a happy family. He never asked her why she wanted to have lunch with him nor did she ever give a reason. His marriage was not happy, and he told her about it and about his children, whom he loved greatly.

He was in love with her personality and her sexual aroma. Sometimes he was sad, because nothing was to be done.

This went on for about ten years. He and his wife separated and divorced, but his lunch partner was still happily married. She had told her husband that she was lunching with him, and he had no idea what her husband thought. They would see each other occasionally, and her husband was friendly. He suspected that she had told him that he was lonely in his marriage and wanted a woman friend. This, of course, was true.

He remarried at sixty, marrying a woman he had known slightly for many years. She was a magical person who met his yearning for love and intimacy, which had been stifled by his marriage. He was deeply in love. As a result, the monthly lunches stopped.

Both Reid and Alice felt that it was no longer appropriate and no longer needed on his part. He occasionally saw her at parties, and they would enjoy talking. She was just as attractive as ever to him, and he sensed that she felt the same, but these were brief sparks of attachment.

Life went on and was good as he and his wife moved into their seventies. Then his wife had a stroke at age eighty. She recovered to some degree, but they sold their home and moved into a retirement home where she could be looked after. She was as sweet and gentle as ever. One leg did not work, but her mind was clear. She read a lot and watched television, and their relationship was as good as ever. But they got out less and saw fewer friends. Then one day, she died from another stroke at age eighty-five.

He was desolate. His mother had died when he was eight years old, and he had felt a sense of loss all of his life. It had never left him. He perhaps needed intimacy more than others. Its absence in his first marriage had deepened the feeling of loss and was perhaps to blame as much as anything else for the problems in the marriage.

Now that his wife was gone, he was terribly lonely, and the yearning for intimacy was stronger than ever. He and his old friend would talk on the telephone from time to time, but there were no lunches.

This went on for a year or two, and then her husband died. At the visitation before the service, she held his hand and kissed him with tenderness. This gave him what he thought was encouragement.

A month or so later, he called and asked her for lunch. They picked up where they had left off years before.

After a few months, she told him that she was selling her house and moving to a different retirement home. He was surprised. His hope had been that they might live together or at least be in the same place.

She knew that he wanted an explanation but found it difficult to explain herself. She began hesitantly. "I don't think that I was very good at marriage. I loved my husband, but I am a loner. I like my independence. You remember how I used to take trips by myself. I needed to get away. You were a respite for me as well. I was fond of you and still am. But I cannot make another commitment. Can't we go on as we did in the past, as loving friends?"

He was quiet and accepting. The deep yearning for love within was not to be fulfilled. He would go on as he had for years, still yearning, still unfulfilled. This was his life at the end of life. He would have to make the best of it. But then he had an insight and wrote her a note,

"I don't want or need a lover. I want a loving friend." She relied,

"You have one, as always."

Chapter 3

FATHER AND SON

Edward and his son, Edward Jr. had lunch together every so often at the University Club in Chicago. The father, who was a member, always paid. He was a successful lawyer. The son was an editor of a local magazine. The father was in his early seventies and the son was in his fifties. He had never married. He had had emotional difficulties finding himself in his twenties but had gradually found himself in a writing and editing career.

The father believed that they had a good relationship. They traded ideas about books on history and politics. The father was a Democrat and the son a Republican, but this did not seem to be a problem. The son was an apostle of "self help" and a critic of government welfare programs. His own struggles to find himself had shaped his politics.

They were at lunch one day when the son began to denounce social programs that encouraged "dependency" on recipients.

The father interjected words that he later regretted. "How can you be critical of people who receive government assistance when you received our financial help when you were out of work and floundering in your twenties?"

His son's face turned red. He threw his napkin down on the table and stood. "You ruined my life. You cared about your career and didn't care about me or my sister Mary You moved us to Chicago so you could join a big law practice and then you were off in Washington when I needed you. When I told you that I was having problems, you didn't pay attention. You cared only about your own career."

This was a shock to his father. His son left the table, and he was alone with his confusion. He sat for a minute and tried to compose himself. It was true that he had moved the family from a small city to Chicago when his children were about to enter high school. The offer of a partnership in an important law firm was too tempting. His wife had welcomed the move and the new, more interesting city. He had not considered the effects on his son and daughter. His daughter had adapted easily and was now happily married and had raised a family. After two years in Chicago, the father had commuted to Washington with a senior partner in his firm to work for two years in the Carter administration. He and his wife had decided not to move to Washington, but he came home often.

His son had always done well in school. He was, perhaps, like his father, a hard working overachiever. He had not revealed any emotional problems that his father took seriously. He did remember his son telling him that he was unhappy in his new school and how he missed his home town, but his father had discounted all that as part of a move. After the son graduated from college he could not decide what to do and began to suffer from depression. His parents knew very little about psychiatry but sought advice and found a doctor to help their son. They paid for the doctor and supported their son financially for two years. It was a painful time, but he had gradually gotten better and found a writing job, which led to a career. He continued to see his doctor. All of this happened after the father had returned home from Washington.

A few days later, the father received a letter.

Dad,

You moved us to Chicago just as I went to high school. That was very hard for me, to make new friends in a new place. I missed my home and old friends. I missed my grandparents who had been an important part of my life. Then, two years later you went off to Washington for two years. You commuted on weekends, but it wasn't the same as having you at home. During my high school years, you were absorbed in your work. I don't think that you thought about our welfare when you moved us, or later. You were absorbed in your career as a big shot lawyer. Your family has meant little to you.

The letter ended. It was a blow to the father, who had thought that he was doing the best for his family by pursuing his career and making a prosperous life for them. His wife had never raised any questions but had gone along with his decisions. It was Saturday, and she was volunteering as a docent at the Chicago Art Institute. So he called his father, who was in his nineties, back in the city they had left. Edward had himself held it against his father when he remarried too soon, he thought, after his mother had died when he was ten. They had worked it out eventually as Edward and his stepmother gradually learned to like each other. His father had often said that children had to learn "to forgive their parents." Edward had told this to his son more than once.

Edward told his father the story and asked for advice.

The old man was ninety-six but still very sharp. "You can't blame yourself for pursuing your career as you did. That was what men of your and my generation were supposed to do. Wives and children were supposed to follow along."

"But Dad, what if I did not pay attention and failed to see warning signs of distress in my son? I admit how intent I was on my work, getting established in a new law firm and going to Washington into the Department of State, doing important work."

"You can't blame yourself. The new generation sees things differently. Marriages are different these days. Wives are different. I know that my grandson is a sensitive person. You have to find a way to get him to see your point of view."

He thanked his dad and waited for his wife to come home. He told her of their son's anger and showed her the letter.

She read it twice, thought for a time and then looked at him. "You were self-centered in the years of our move and your time in Washington. I didn't want you to go and to commute. But you wanted to go so much that I raised no objection. I did want to move to Chicago. I was tired of life in the town where we both grew up and where our parents lived. It was stifling, and life here was exciting. Still, I see his point. Your work was everything to you, probably more important than me or the children. You were much like your law partners and other friends here. I went along with it because we all lived that way. Did you ever ask yourself if the children were happy? I think that you just assumed it, because life on the surface seemed ok."

They had a long talk into the night, and he began to see that she was telling him the truth, telling about a side of himself that he had not seen before. It was very painful. He did not sleep that night and wandered around the house on Sunday, feeling the pain. His wife was sympathetic. She agreed with his father that he was a child of his generation and social class.

Success in work was everything. He had always believed that. What could he do now to repair the damage?

That afternoon he called the rector of his Episcopal church and told him the story. "I am so confused," he told the kindly, soft spoken priest. "I cannot separate my 'sins' from my ambitions. My professional ambitions were perhaps good, but my 'sin' that is my neglect of my son was part of my ambitions. How do I confess my sins without denying my ambitions?"

The priest's words were clear. "You could have followed your ambitions and still have given more attention to your son, daughter, and wife. But your professional ambition was everything to you. You were just beginning your law practice here. You did not need to leave your family and go to Washington. You could have stayed here and helped the family settle in after a big change in their way of life."

He was listening. "I see that now. I think you are right. But what do I do now? I have lost my son. How do I get him back?"

"It may take some time. I would write him and tell him what he has taught you. Say that you feel like a character in a novel in whom the good and bad are tangled together. Ask for his help in getting untangled." The priest had another idea. "What have the two of you most enjoyed doing together?"

He thought a minute. "Going to baseball games and fly fishing."

"Ask him to go fishing as soon as he can and suggest that you go see a Cubs game."

He wrote the letter and brought his fishing equipment down for the attic and waited for a reply.

Chapter 4

A Daring Decision

Roger was unhappy in his marriage. They had married too quickly before they really knew each other. It was not long before their differences caused daily frictions. He wanted to rule the roost, and she was determined to have her own way. Their three children, a daughter and twin sons, came early, and the business of family life disguised the tensions, and all seemed happy on the surface. They gloried in their talented children. They spent their vacations at a summer home on a lake in Wisconsin. She and the children would go there for two months in July and August, and he would take a week here and there. He was a very busy investment banker.

He and his wife had separate lives. She was active in civic affairs, and he had his work. As he reached the age of sixty, he began to think of retirement a few years down the road but could not imagine what he would do. He had no hobbies. He liked to travel, and they had enjoyed good trips, but one could not travel endlessly. He had never been a volunteer. Work had been his life.

He could sense that he was attractive to women and had enjoyed this without reflecting on it. Then he had to reflect. He met a woman at a cocktail party who intrigued him. She had black hair, dark eyes, and high cheek bones. She was exotic. She taught French literature at a local university and, she told him, went to France every summer.

"She likes me," he thought. He didn't think that his wife liked him very much so this was a pleasant thought.

She told him that she had been married to a prominent surgeon but had been divorced for some time. Her only child, a daughter, was at school in France for the year. He told her something about himself and mentioned that his mother had lived in Paris in the nineteen twenties and that he had found some of her French friends in Paris in past years.

They were just enjoying a mutual attraction when the hostess, who was skillful at moving her guests around so that no one would get bored, moved her along. He and his wife never stayed together at cocktail parties, and he kept looking for his new acquaintance and finally saw her standing alone. He couldn't help himself.

"I would like to see you again," he said.

She smiled. "I would enjoy that."

"Might we have lunch?"

"Yes, but where?"

"I could come to the campus."

"Do you know many people at the university?"

"Yes, at the school of management."

"Perhaps somewhere else then."

She was thinking of protecting him from rumors, but he did not see this. She told him,

"I often take a sandwich to the park and feed the ducks while I eat."

He liked that and they agreed to meet at the large park in the center of the city on a given day. He felt guilty from the beginning as he would not tell his wife. Something was pushing him that could not be denied.

They met at a secluded spot on a weekday and sat on a bench by a little stream. Few people were around. She told him about her marriage. Her husband had left her for a younger medical resident a few years back. She did not miss him. They were very different in temperament. She enjoyed teaching French literature, particularly novels of the nineteenth century. She had written two books of criticism and was well regarded in her field. Her daughter was a student at Swarthmore, who was taking her junior year abroad in Paris.

He told her about himself and his children and expressed his disappointment with his marriage. It crossed his mind that perhaps he and her husband were too much alike, but he hoped not. He described himself as lonely. That was not her husband, she said.

They kept meeting in the park at least once a week. They had begun to hold hands, and one day he kissed her. His sexual temperature was rising. But what was he to do?

Finally, one day he told her, "I love you and want to live with you. How do you feel about it?"

She answered, "I have come to care for you very much. But I do not want to break up a marriage. You must be very sure of what you want and must be willing to face the consequences, which may be painful. I know. I have been through this. It will be painful for you, your wife, and especially your children."

He had not thought about consequences. He wanted to be with her. He was absolutely sure that he could no long live in an unhappy marriage. It was damaging to him and also to his wife. One Sunday afternoon, he summoned up his courage and told his wife that he wanted a divorce. He had found someone else.

She was furious. "I will not stand for this. You go see this woman, whoever she is, and get out of whatever entanglement you are in. Otherwise I will tell the children. They won't stand for it either."

He called his new love that afternoon and told her what his wife had said.

She listened carefully. "Would you like time to think about this? Perhaps we should not see each other for a while."

"No. My mind is made up. If I put it off, I would only be pretending to stay, and I want to leave, right today if necessary."

So he left. He packed a bag and drove away in his Lexus. The car was fortunately in his name. They went to a house in the country that she owned. It was wonderful. He had not been so happy in years. They slept well, ate big breakfasts, took long walks, and talked and talked. He enjoyed physical love like he had never really known. He canceled all his appointments at work and didn't care if he ever went back.

After ten days, they went back to town to her small house. He took a few more days but called his secretary, who was his friend and had been with him for years.

"Your wife sent your clothes to the office," his secretary told him. "She has filed for divorce. Your twin sons have each written saying that that they do not want to see you again. I have not heard from your daughter. Your partners, Tom and Frank, tell me that they are with you but their wives are not. When are you coming in?"

He called his lawyer, who was also a close friend and asked for advice.

"Your wife has her own money," said his lawyer, "so I doubt that she can take much from you so long as you pay for the education of the children. I would let her have the house in Wisconsin and the house in town. Just ease out as easily as you can. Your friends are not surprised that you want a divorce. Anyone could see flaws in your marriage. They are surprised about your romance, and I suspect that some are a bit jealous. Your friends are also your wife's friends, so you will be lonely for a time. You will have to build a new life."

His daughter, who was a rising senior in college, called and expressed some understanding. She knew that the marriage was not good. "Why did you leave so abruptly? Do you know what you are doing? Who is this woman? How well do you know her?"

He did his best to explain, and she promised to meet both of them in town before she returned to college.

"But if I accept this, Mother will cut me off," she said. "She is furious."

He asked her to talk with the boys and explain as best she could, and she promised to try.

In the days that followed, he found a good divorce lawyer, who advised him to be as generous as possible. The existence of another woman was not in his favor, but he was not deserting a family that needed his financial help. It was finally settled on a no-fault basis. He was free but without moorings.

The two lovers went to France to meet her daughter. She was a bright, charming girl, not unlike her mother. Then they came home, and he had to find a new life. She began to teach in September, and he went back to work. He made a few new friends on the faculty, especially a historian whom he particularly liked. They decided to marry at Christmas in hopes of giving his sons time to reconcile.

He was lonely and missed his sons, who were still home. His daughter was away at school. One Saturday afternoon in early September, he was sitting at home in her study. She was running errands. He noticed a copy of Voltaire's *Candide* on the shelf and took it down. It was in French, but he could read it. On the last page Dr. Pangloss advises Candide to face life by cultivating his "jardin."

That's what I'll do, he said to himself. "I'll plant a fall garden – lettuce and butternut squash." He had worked in a garden years before during the second world war when his parents had a "Victory Garden" and would do it again. It would be lots of fun and serve as a symbol for his new life.

Chapter 5

TWO BROTHERS

The two brothers were very different. Sam was a great success in the eyes of the world as a corporation lawyer. He represented the rich and the worthy, at least worthy in their own eyes. Will was an accountant in a small firm. The clients were small businesses – real estate firms and clothing stores and the like. Sam went to Princeton and Michigan law school. Will went to a small college. They both lived in Kansas City but in different social worlds. Sam married the daughter of a bank president. Will's father-in-law was an insurance agent. Sam's children went to private schools, and Will's went to public schools. Sam went to an Episcopal church, and Will joined his wife's Methodist church. Sam belonged to the country club, and Will did not.

Sam was two years older than Will. His achievements had always been in Will's sight, but Will was never ever to keep up. Their parents had been proud of Sam's progress step by step. They were nice to Will, but disappointment floated around him, and he knew it. Sam was very self-confident. Will was not ambitious, but he liked himself. He loved his wife and two children. They lived a good, modest life among good, modest friends.

Sam's wife was active in civic life in more organizations than she could count. She and Sam led somewhat separate lives, because they were both so busy. Their children were independent and ambitious in school, sports, and among their friends. Will's children were happy but not particularly ambitious. His daughter wanted to be a nurse, and his son hoped to be a baseball coach. He was a very good player.

The brothers ate lunch together occasionally, but the two families saw little of each other, even at holidays. The cousins did not know each other well. Sam's children eventually went to Princeton, and Will's went to the state university at Columbia. Their grandfather had been a high school principal, so Sam was a self-made man in a sense. Will lacked the drive, but he was not a failure in his own eyes. He accepted life as it came. Sam had always challenged life to give him more of what he wanted, success as he defined it.

When Will became fifty, he asked himself if he was a "success" and answered yes. He enjoyed his work and served his clients well. His family life was happy. He was not rich like Sam, but his income was pretty good. He had never expected to make a mark on the world. He did not see any need for an overriding purpose in his life. He tried to apply the lessons he heard in sermons in church to his life. Methodists had strong social ethics, which he tried to follow.

Sam did not ask himself if he was successful, because it was self-evident. Nor did he ask about any larger purposes of his life. His work gave him enough purpose. One day a friend called and invited him to attend a talk by a guest speaker at St. Mark's, their church. The speaker was a psychologist who was to talk to a group of middle-aged men about the "mid-life crisis." Sam could not imagine what that was but agreed to go out of curiosity.

Most of the middle-aged men in the room knew each other well and would have been deemed successful by standards of the day. The speaker did not look like them. He was casually dressed in a slightly rumpled way. He did not lecture but talked in a conversational way. He described a recent study of middle-aged men that explored how they were living at mid-life. Long interviews had been conducted with the participants of the study and with their wives. The findings had not been fully anticipated. They were divided into two clusters. One group did not feel that they had been successful in their work and professions. They had missed the marks that they had set for themselves. A number of them compensated for this supposed failure by reappraising their lives and searching for new ways to live and work beyond the conventional boundaries of success. A few changed occupations. One became a minister, another a baseball coach, another a nurse. Some looked inward to Yoga and more contemplative lives.

The even more interesting finding was that a good many of those who judged themselves to have been successful had begun to question the value of getting ahead. Perhaps it was not enough. The research project itself may have stimulated the question. There was no denying the restlessness. This was not true of all of the strivers. Some kept on going. But a fair number began to ask questions. Work was less satisfying. The round of their busy lives seemed to be less rhythmic. They began to ask themselves how to open doors to a richer life, not knowing what that might be. The study captured some of this, more companionship with their wives and children, new attention to friendship, volunteering to tutor dis-advantaged children. They were trying to find what might be called authentic experience.

Sam listened to the talk carefully but could not see how it applied to him. He was happy in his professional success. He went home and told his wife, Polly, about the talk. To his surprise, she posed.

"I wonder if our lives are not too one-dimensional ?" she asked

"What do you mean?"

"For the past twenty years, we have been intent on getting ahead, being prominent, making money. Perhaps it is time for us to 'smell the flowers' more?"

Sam was puzzled. "But I like what I am doing. I like being a successful lawyer. Don't you enjoy your life? You are certainly busy enough, doing good things."

She said that she wasn't sure. There was a great deal of pretense and snobbery in her volunteer life. Much of her activity seemed designed to make the volunteers feel good. It was not clear that the recipients benefitted.

Nothing was resolved but her questions had planted some doubts in his mind.

The next week, Will called and invited Sam to a Kansas City Royals baseball game. They were playing the Red Sox, and a client had given Will two box seats on the first base line. Sam accepted, and that night they skipped dinner for hot dogs and cold beer at the game. It was a close, high-scoring game that the Royals won.

At one point, Sam turned to Will and said, "I have not had so much fun in years."

Will then asked Sam, on the spur of the moment, "Would you like to go fly fishing in the Ozarks next week? Charley and I were planning to go, but he can't make it."

Sam said yes without even thinking about it.

The following week, they put their gear in Will's old station wagon and headed south into the Ozarks in search of a river they knew that was full of trout. They stayed in a cabin near the river, cooked their own meals, mostly steak, pancakes, and eggs, and caught beautiful, glistening, fat brown trout. They kept and ate only a few and threw the rest back.

One day while they were both standing in midstream in their hip boots, Sam said, "Why haven't we done this more often? I love it."

They were gone four days, and Sam didn't want to go home and shave and put on a necktie and go to work. On Monday morning, he called his secretary to say that he was taking another day off. Then he turned to Polly. "Why don't we go to the Nelson Gallery and see the new exhibit of American impressionist paintings? We could have lunch there. "

She delightedly accepted. They had a fine time. He liked Childe Hassam's patriotic pictures and Mary Cassat's scenes of domestic life. He drank a beer with his crab cakes at lunch, and it tasted so good.

When they were finishing, he said to Polly, "Would you like to go to the movies? Let's see what's on at the Plaza."

They saw the Marx Brothers film Duck Soup, and he laughed so hard he could hardly breathe.

He went to work the next day but came home at noon and told Polly, "I have turned two of my cases over to my partners. How would you like to go to Paris? When we get back I am going to look into more pro bono work in the firm, after Will and I go fishing again."

Polly was happy. "Let's go. From now on we are going to travel light."

Chapter 6

A LONELY LIFE

Louise thought that her life had not been what she wanted. She had gone to Columbia University and studied to become a librarian. Then she had worked at the Library of Congress during World War II, but it had come to nothing. She had never been promoted. Her father died after the war, and she went home to a midwestern city to live with her Mother. She became the librarian for a local company that made and sold veterinary medicines, but that didn't work out. The family owned an office building downtown, and she decided to oversee the management herself. This was the entire income for her and her mother.

She was the baby of the family, who came ten years after her brother and sister. They seemed to her to be the favored ones. Their grandmother had dressed them in white and spent lots of time with them. She felt left out. Her brother had become a successful architect who died young without a wife or family. Her sister had married with one son but had died of pneumonia as a young woman.

Her nephew kept in touch with her and her mother but lived at a distance. He saw them about once a year. Once when he was in town, the president of what had been his great grandfather's bank and the manager of the office building, asked him to meet in order to discuss her ownership. They told him stories of how difficult she was and urged him to try to get her to soften her style. He listened but did nothing, because he knew that nothing could be done.

It seemed to him that she was determined to be unhappy. She had been alone all her life and kept others at a distance, except for her own mother, on whom she was emotionally dependent. When her mother died, she was even more isolated except for a handful of family friends.

The one thing that she did for others was to volunteer to read to small children in the local municipal library on Saturday mornings. She had always loved children's literature, especially the European classics. The children were not yet reading, but they could follow stories. She enjoyed reading to them, because they listened and enjoyed and were not a problem. They appreciated her.

One day, she decided to tell them a true story. Her grandmother had eloped with a young man about whom her prominent family was not at all sure. They had gone west to Denver where he worked in a bank. Her mother had heard the story from the young bride herself. After a year in Denver, the young couple decided to go back home to be reconciled.

They traveled by wagon train, and one night as they sat around the fire with a group of wagons, she said to him, "Charlie, I think I hear Father's voice."

They followed the voice and found her father sitting around another fire. He was headed west on business. There was no need to reconcile. They were happy just to see each other. In another year, they went back home and began a family.

The children loved the story and wanted to know more about her family. So she told more stories, some true and some made up, about frontier life and the Civil War and life in the west. One of her grandfather's brothers had been a colorful mayor of Colorado Springs, and she told stories about him as well as about her rancher uncles, with whom she had spent time as a girl.

For the first time in her life, she felt needed and appreciated. Her life had not been a failure.

Chapter 7

A New Career

Dorothy was a "personal banker" who advised clients on their investments. She had studied finance in college and earned an MBA afterward. It was the nineteen fifties, and the lives of her friends did not appeal to her – marriage, babies, tennis at the country club, and more babies. She liked men and got along with them easily. Executives in the bank treated her as if she were another man, with one exception. Once she had become a "personal banker" they did not promote her. She had good clients and was well paid, but that was the end of it.

Her close women friends were independent professionals, a pediatrician, a social worker, and a school principal. They played golf at the club on times set aside for women, had a book club, and took trips together. Her clients were well-to-do men and their widows and sometimes their children. She had learned how to help people achieve financial security given the means available, which were usually comfortable if not substantial.

Her brother was president of a manu-facturing company, and she served on his board. He and his wife were her best friends, and their children were very fond of their doting aunt. She spent holidays with them and went to Europe with them more than once. She grew up in St. Mark's Episcopal church where her father and then her brother were on the vestry. She was invited to join the vestry when women were included but declined. She saw the church as just "the country club at prayer." She could glimpse an elusive spiritual reality in the prayers and liturgy but had never tried to explore it.

In 1995, she had her sixty-fifth birthday. No one suggested that she retire from the bank. Nor did she want to retire. Still, she decided that she should talk with someone, so she made an appointment with the bank president. He was an old friend who smiled and waited for her to speak.

"Well Charlie," she said, "what do you think I should do?"

"You mean about retirement?"

"Yes. What do you think?"

"You don't have to go. I was not going to suggest it. You are a valuable asset to the bank. You should certainly stay until you are seventy, and perhaps longer. What would you like to do?"

"I want to stay. Retirement does not appeal to me. What would I do if I retired? I have seen men die from idleness in retirement. I am healthy, but I can't work in this job forever. What if we shoot for seventy and have this conversation again?"

"That's fine with me, Dorothy, although I may be gone by then, since I am sixty-eight now. Peggy is urging me to slack off. I am thinking of going into business with my son in a small investment firm. So, who knows?"

They left it at that. She began to talk with her friends about their intentions. The doctor hoped to work part time and forever. A lawyer who worked with wills and estates had the same idea. The social worker was worried, because she could not stay in her agency much longer. The school principal was planning to move to a house on the beach with a friend.

One friend, Ellen, was independently wealthy and had never worked at a job but had served any number of charities for years. One day she said to Dorothy, "I notice that the boards of the organizations I help are run by men and women in their fifties. The older people fall away for some reason. I feel increasingly out of touch."

The two friends seemed at loose ends in their musings, and then Ellen had an idea. "Why don't we go on a retreat? I have a friend who visits a Buddhist monastery near San Luis Obispo from time to time. She loves it. She says she can think clearly when she is there. You don't have to be a Buddhist. They have classes and so on, but you can just be there if you want nothing else."

Dorothy liked the idea. She knew only that Buddhism was peaceful and did not know much more about it. So they made a reservation, packed their bags, and went.

The monastery was a collection of low buildings among a grove of spreading trees and green lawns. Visitors stayed in a lodge and ate together. The monks, in saffron robes, lived in other buildings and mingled easily with the guests. Most of the monks, but not all, were Asian. Classes on spiritual topics were offered, and all were invited to times and places for meditation. The atmosphere was quiet and peaceful.

Ellen and Dorothy slept better than they had in ages and ate the good, simple food with enthusiasm. By mid-week, they had joined a class on meditation taught by a round, jolly Tibetan monk, who laughed all the time. It took them a few days to learn the rudiments of meditation, and just as they began to enjoy it, they realized that it was Friday, and they were to leave on Sunday.

Ellen had to go back to Alameda for a dental appointment. Dorothy didn't want to go and asked the Lodge if she could stay another week. Ellen was ready to go. She had gotten the relaxation that she had come for, but Dorothy wanted something more; she was not sure what.

After the second week, she called the bank and told them that she would stay one more week and then come back to work, but at the end of that week, she did not want to go home. She went to see the abbot, a Chinese American, who told her that before he became a monk, he had been in a family grocery business in San Francisco.

He was just like the president of her bank in his approach. "Well, Dorothy what do you want to do?"

"I don't know. I like it here. I am happy. But I can't stay on as a paying guest."

"Well, there is another possibility. We have been looking for someone to manage our investments. Eric, a former broker, who is now a monk and has been doing it for some years, would like to give it up. Would you like to take it on?"

"But I am not a monk or even a Buddhist."

"That doesn't matter. You could either go back to the bank and do it from there or stay here. Which would you like to do?"

She could go home and take on the new account with regular trips to the monastery. But that didn't feel right. "Why don't I move in here and tackle the job? We can decide where I live later. For right now, I like it here. And I am halfway through my course on meditation."

The future would take care of itself. She was sure of that.

Chapter 8

An Uncertain Marriage

Mark was away consulting on a difficult medical case. He came to a conclusion quickly, so he called for a reservation to fly home a day early. He called home and the line was busy, so he got on the plane just in time to get home that night.

His car pulled into the driveway at ten o'clock, and he left it there. As he entered the house, he heard two voices upstairs – his wife's and that of a man and laughter. He went into the living room and sat down quietly in the dark.

Not long after that, his friend George came down the stairs and went out the front door.

He was not sure what to do. It was quiet upstairs. Finally, he left his wife a note on the hall table and left. "You were busy tonight, so I have gone to Sugar Lake for the night. We can talk tomorrow."

They had a country house at Sugar Lake. He drove there and, with the help of a double scotch whiskey, went to bed and slept, but not well. He was a doctor and was used to little sleep.

He got up on Saturday morning, made breakfast, and waited to see if she would call. He thought that they had a good marriage. They had met when he was a resident in surgery. She was a nurse, and they had been thrown together in the whirl of hospital life. She had provided the emotional support and steadiness he needed. They married after he began his practice. She gave up nursing for children and the life of a busy doctor's wife. Her life now was centered around the country club – tennis, bridge, and parties. Their children were grown.

She called early. "Mark, I am so sorry. What can I say?"

"What do you have to say?"

"I have no interest in George. He and Dorothy are getting a divorce. He came to me just to talk about it, and we have been having lunch together. He is lonely in his marriage, because she is all caught up in her many volunteer activities. I talked to him about my loneliness, and he understood. It was no more than that."

"Why didn't you tell me that you were unhappy?"

"I did not know how to tell you. You are so busy in your own life. Have you not noticed?"

"No, but you know how busy I am. You can talk to me now."

"We lead separate lives. You work long hours and seem to be preoccupied with the pressures of your practice. I lead a nice, pretty vacant life as a doctor's wife with nothing much to do except enjoy myself. It's not enough."

"What would you like to do?"

"I don't know. More than anything, I want to talk with you and get close to you again."

He said nothing for a moment. "I'm not sure what I want to do. I don't like it here by myself, but I'm not ready to come home. The thought of you in bed with Owen is more than I can handle. I will stay here a few days and go to work from here." He thought of this as a kind of punishment. He wanted to hurt her as she had hurt him.

She began to cry. "I am so sorry. Please forgive me. I want you to come home. We must talk. Why put it off?"

"Why don't we talk on the telephone?"

"That's a good idea. Can we begin now?"

He agreed, and she began by telling him about her life. He had his work, which was all consuming. She had enjoyed nursing but had given it up to have children and create the home and family life that he expected. She could have gone back to work after the children were in college. She was interested in a course in special surgery, but he did not want her to do it. He had enough surgery in his life already. So she had fallen back into the easy life that he provided. They took trips with the children and went to Europe several times. She had good friends, mostly doctors' wives, and enjoyed their lives in common. She had worked as a part-time nurse in a clinic for poor people, but the clinic had closed for lack of funds.

He confessed that he had no idea that she was unhappy with her life.

"I have been lonely in the marriage," she told him. "Haven't you been lonely?"

"No. My life is full of people, patients, doctors, friends with whom I play golf and see at parties. I love to see the children when they come home."

"But we have lost the closeness, the intimacy that we had in our life together, especially when the children were young. We shared the adventure of a family."

"I never thought of that. Maybe you're right. But what do you want me to do? I am not going to give up practicing medicine."

"I don't want you to do that."

"What do you want?"

"I'm not sure."

That was their first conversation. They continued talking once a day but did not seem to be getting anywhere. She wanted to fill the loneliness in her life but was not sure how. He had no idea how to help her. After two weeks of conversations, nothing was resolved. He admitted that he was still angry about George, and all she could say was that she was sorry and she wanted him to come home. He wanted to go home but was still angry and too stubborn to admit it.

So they agree to give it a rest. They lived apart, and eventually their children and friends learned about it.

His daughter, Mary, called him and took her Mother's part. "Dad, I don't know what started all this, but Mom is unhappy and wants you to come home. What's wrong? Why won't you go?"

He did not want Mary to have the full story, so there was not much for him to say. It looked as if he had left for no reason. This was the explanation that went around among their friends. He kept on working as hard as ever but enjoyed it less. He missed her but did not want to admit it, even to himself.

The summer dragged on into fall. His wife wrote him a letter, which he answered, but nothing came of it. His son wanted to bring his family home for Thanksgiving, but his father was vague about it, so there was no trip. Mary and her family were in town, and her mother went to her house for Thanksgiving. He had dinner at his club by himself.

Then one day he received a letter inviting him to lead a surgery clinic in Bangalore, India in December. It would be for a two-week period over Christmas. This gave him the excuse he wanted. He called her. "How would you like to go to India?"

"India – where, when, and why?"

"I have been asked to work in a clinic in Bangalore, and I will need a good nurse. Will you do it?"

"Of course. When do we leave?"

"I will be home today, and we will make plans for the trip. This will be an adventure. I thought that we might see something of India while we are there, so we can decide what we want to see. I have been working one day a week in a clinic for indigent patients and will do more of that when we come back. Perhaps you could help there as well."

Something had been released in him, and she could feel it. "Oh," she thought, "whatever it is, keep it coming, and I will meet it with all the feeling I have."

They were starting over on a new adventure, and this one would last.

Chapter 9

THE KINDNESS OF HORSES

Emory had loved animals from the time he was a boy. His family always had wonderful dogs, and he learned to appreciate the intelligence of cats when one walked into the house and adopted them. A family that raised goats lived not too far from them. One day his friend, from that family, offered to give him a baby goat, surely without permission. He carried the little black and white baby goat home and right into the front hallway.

His father, who was standing on the upstairs landing, said, "Take that goat right back where you found it."

There was no discussion. The goat went home. In later years, his father apologized. "I should have let you keep that goat."

There would have been room for it. They lived with his grandmother in a large lot that was double, front and back, with a big barn in the far back yard. A baby goat is fine, but what do you do with a grown-up goat?

His school was only two blocks away from home, and he loved it. His mother had gone to the same school. A friend of hers told him in later years that "Gladys used to faint in school from time to time, and everyone got to go home, so they were often hoping that she would faint." She was not thought to be strong. Many years later, when he read her diary, he found occasional references to her feeling ill but without any medical explanation.

Then, when he was eight years old, his life changed in less than a week. His mother had been downtown shopping. It was a warm January day. He was standing on the porch when she came up the front walk. She was seemingly so tired that she could hardly walk. He remembered that they put her to bed, and she went to the hospital soon after. That was Saturday. She had pneumonia. It was 1939, and there were no antibiotics.

Children were not allowed in hospitals in those days, so on Wednesday night, he and his father went up the fire escape to see her. She was in her nightgown with her hair down, and he would never forget the joyous hug she gave him when they went into her room.

He went to school on Friday morning and came home to lunch as he usually did. As he was walking up to the house, he noticed family friends that he recognized in the front room and knew that something was wrong. His father took him upstairs to his room and told that his mother had died.

He remembered feeling sad and numb, but he did not cry. He did remember asking his Father to promise not to marry again and getting yes as the answer. He could not remember anything else about the days that followed. He did not attend her funeral nor even know when it was held. His Father told him years later that his grandmother had thought it was a bad idea.

Life went on during spring. Then one day as he was hanging around a riding academy that was near his school and home, he saw a small horse in a stall and asked about him. He was not an academy horse but was stabled there temporarily by the owner, a Mr. Pyle, who owned horses. His name was Chubby, and he was 14 hands high, half horse, half pony. Emory suddenly wanted to own Chubby in the worst way. He went home and told his father, and that weekend they went down to Mr. Pyle's stables south of town, where Chubby had been moved. Not only did they buy Chubby, but his Father also bought a proud looking black horse named Sandy. The horses came home the next day and were put in the barn in the back yard.

He knew nothing about horses and had to learn fast. His father taught him to post in the saddle and explained about the different gaits – walk, trot, rack, and gallop. Emory used a "Kentucky" saddle, which was a padded English saddle. He was put in charge of the horses – feeding and watering them and cleaning out their stalls and putting down fresh straw. From that day until early winter, Emory rode Chubby on the many available bridle paths. They put the horses on a farm south of town for the winter and went down to ride them regularly.

Chubby was his best friend. He taught the horse to jump over small heights. The horse knew what he wanted him to do. One day that summer, he was out riding, and he developed a terrible anger. He did not know what he was angry about, but the anger was fierce. When they returned to the barn, he got down off Chubby and took the reins and began to beat the horse on his neck with the reins. He remembered the look of terror in Chubby's eyes as he tried to move away. He suddenly realized what he was doing and began to cry with great sobs. He put his arms about Chubby's neck and begged the horse to forgive him.

His father broke his promise and remarried after two years. They had to move to an apartment across town to a new school, and Chubby and Sandy had to go away. Chubby went to a cousin in a nearby city. He lost his best friend, his school, and his father all at once. He didn't like his stepmother either.

His love of animals caused him to become a veterinarian with large animals, mostly on farms – cows, pigs, horses – although he would look after anything from chickens to dogs and cats.

He did this for years and loved it, but by the time he was seventy, he began to ease off, especially with the large animals.

Retirement was not easy. He was used to an active outdoor life. He had a vegetable garden and planted flowers, but life somehow seemed empty. He and his wife had been regular churchgoers, and she seemed satisfied with this. She did not worry about God or the future or about anything after death. She was content in her earthly happiness with him, her children and grandchildren and friends. But that was not enough for him. He wanted more, but what did he want? He had read enough about religion to learn that religious faith seemed to speak to a human reach for the infinite, for some ultimate longing that ordinary life could not give. But if there was such a gift, where was it, and how could he find it?

He talked to his minister about his longings, but nothing came of it. Ordinary prayer seemed hollow. He talked with a close Jewish friend, who told him to stop worrying. Judiasm taught one to live a good life and trust in the future. It was good advice, but he wanted more. His minister recommended a psychotherapist who worked as a "spiritual" adviser, whatever that was. So he went to see her.

She listened to him talk about his life, including his childhood, and his work, and then made a comment. "You have been an applied scientist, a person who used his left brain to solve problems. You must start listening to your heart and your right brain."

Step by step she taught him to meditate, to find a calm center in himself, to invoke the right side of his brain to experience beauty and color and warm feelings. She introduced him to C.S. Lewis and other writers who talked about the surprise when "grace" came into one's life.

He felt a lot better. He began to go to the Episcopal church, where he could experience beauty and color. The bread and wine of the Eucharist were gifts he did not have to work for. They were just there.

But he was not a contemplative. He wanted to work, to do something. One day he was having lunch with a fellow veterinarian, who began to tell about "equine therapy." It was therapy on horseback. First, one learned to care for a horse, to feed and groom it, and to provide for a clean stall, and exercise. One was to earn the horse's trust and trust the horse in turn. Horses learn from us, and we may learn from them. Riding a horse may create calmness and reduce stress. A feeling of companionship is the key. Riding a horse may provide a rhythm that enhances muscle tone, balance, and coordination. These were practical findings without much verification in the research literature. They went far enough.

He was intrigued and searched for and found a woman who provided "equine therapy." She made no great claims to help people beyond the centering and calmness that looking after and riding horses may give. He could not make himself into a therapist, but he could teach people to take care of and ride horses and went to work for her part time. It was as if he and Chubby were together again.

Chapter 10

FINDING A PLACE

It was a small city, its population less than one hundred thousand, set on a river bank and reaching inland to high bluffs. It was settled in the 1840s by Kentuckians and Virginians who had traveled west with fresh hopes. The town became a jumping-off point to the West before and after the Civil War. A sign on the city limits said, "Welcome where southern hospitality meets western democracy."

People worked in flour mills, packing plants, and hardware companies and lived modest lives as most people do. A relatively small number of "old families" owned and ran such companies and were bankers, lawyers, and doctors, an upper crust with a good opinion of itself with a business class beneath it. There was continuity of family position over time in business and the professions.

Matthew was born into an old family that had kept its status but lost its wealth. His great great grandfather came from Kentucky as the first doctor in the county after the land had been purchased from Indian tribes by the US government. His great grandfather had come as a poor boy from Virginia and married the doctor's daughter. He then went into her uncle's bank and, in time, became president of the bank and a prominent citizen. His grandfather, born to wealth, squandered it, and died poor. His daughter married a young outsider who prospered in business, but the patrimony was broken. He carried the social cachet of "old family" without the substance.

This was perhaps a blessing. He had to find his way in the world. His father gave him an education, opportunity, and ambition. He did not want to be a businessman or a banker. He thought about the law, but it was too much like business to him. So he went to graduate school and became a professor, although not at first. He had to work his way up. He did this by teaching well and writing books. He was a specialist in modern American political history, particularly of presidents. He knew the presidents of the twentieth century like old friends, with an enemy or two.

He had grown up in the company of friends who had gone to school and church together since kindergarten. They had dispersed to different colleges, but he was the only one who did not return to live. Eventually they married local girls from families they knew and settled down to stable, perhaps uneventful lives. It was always good to see them when he came home.

One summer he was trying to finish a book. The research had been done, and he was writing. He decided to go for a month and write and got an office at a local college to do his work. His wife came along, but she found the town suffocating. His children were in college and found other places to go. He and his wife rented a house in a neighborhood that that he knew. His parents were old but living well, and he spent more time with them than he had in years. He went to lunch often with his friends. It was as if he had never been away.

A good many things had changed. The World War II generation was dying off. Many had come home after the war to go into family businesses and professions. Others had found good niches.

It was a much larger group than his small cluster of "depression babies." He did not know many of that generation very well and was sorry for that, because they were attractive and interesting. Nor did he know their children well, because they were just that much younger. There were fewer of them around, because the economy was changing and continuity was lessening. The old industries were dying and new ones were coming, along with new people to run them. When he went to the country club for dinner, he saw fewer familiar faces. His mother and father had a few friends left, a diminishing number.

After that summer, he came home less often. His work was engaging. He went abroad to teach twice, once in England, once in France. Two of his friends divorced and moved away, taking their work with them. Then he had a spot of trouble. He and his wife divorced after a long spell of unhappiness. There was no one to blame. It just happened.

The children had gone off to lead lives of their own. For the first time in his life, he was lonely. He was nearing retirement age and was tired of teaching. He had always been an enthusiastic teacher who gave much time to his students. And then, he was tired of them. He did not enjoy grading and evaluating. Their work fell short of accomplishment, good as it often was. His graduate students had trouble finding good jobs, because there were always too many on the market. His department colleagues seemed increasingly petty and selfish, and their unceasing wrangling with each other bored him. University administrators sought prestige for the school by rewarding professional publication, and the work could be good, but he could not find any celebration of purpose beyond academic prestige.

He realized that he had substituted university life for the community in which he had grown up, having stayed at the same school for his entire career. But the university was changing, with retirements, new leadership, and new waves of students. He would see people, men and women, who must be faculty members in the library and would not know who they were. His own department was led by younger people with new ideas and methods that had outstripped him. Department colloquia in which members gave talks and outside scholars gave papers increasingly became too difficult for him to understand. He would have liked to serve on committees for graduate student dissertations, but he was no longer up to date in the research literature.

He thought of going back to his hometown to live. He could continue to write. Research materials were now available on the computer. Although he was not sure what he wanted to write about. He had plowed the presidential furrow pretty deep. But writing was his life. What else could he do?

So he went for a time, but he found the place changed. One very close friend had died. Two had moved to a nearby large city. A few were left, and that was good. The World War II generation was gone, as were most of their children, and none of the children of his friends lived there. The old haunts were gone, and favorite restaurants had disappeared. Older neighborhoods were run down and shabby, and newer neighborhoods were outside of town. The downtown had died. Office buildings were empty, as were storefronts. The doctors had gone to locations near the highways, as had most commercial development. He had loved to go downtown. He remembered Christmas shopping when he would bump into friends wherever he went.

He was lonely, and for the first time in his life, he did not have a place to live that was determined either by birth or work. What was he to do? He could go back to his university, where he knew people and could continue his scholarship. But he had felt increasingly lonely there. But he had found that he could not go home again, because the home he had known and loved was no longer there.

He knew the answer to his dilemma. A person cannot find complete identity or fulfillment in an institution or a community. Identity is an inner reality. He did not seem to have one, beyond a professional understanding of himself. He began to ask himself who he had been, who he was. Looking back on his teaching, he could see an identity in his close work with students. He wanted to help them. He had never been one of those scholars who looked down on students as not up to the mark. He remembered the great satisfaction that he had gotten from courses well taught and the appreciation that students had expressed to him.

He had once belonged to a Jung Society where the works of Carl Jung were read and discussed. One time a Jungian analyst attended, and they split up into groups to discuss a question that she had raised. He led his small group, and she observed them. He afterwards asked her to give him an example of a Jungian "archetype."

She replied, "You are Hermes, carrying the torch (good news) from one community to another."

He was a teacher, and his deepest satisfactions had come from teaching. His scholarship was also teaching in the form of writing. He was a student of political leader-ship, particularly American presidents. Toward the midpoint of his career, he had seen a pattern in his work on leadership. Politicians must find support for their leadership in the historical context of their national community. What ideals can be articulated and realized in a dynamic historical community that is changing all the time? Political ability is necessary but not sufficient. Followers must come forward. Idealizations of "heroic" presidencies failed to see the importance of context.

He began to see that he had found an identity for himself as a scholar in his writing. He had fostered a romantic engagement for himself with American political history. He could continue to write if he wished, and there was much to say. But he had written a good deal and did not really want to do that any longer. He had never been a very good "social scientist" who would add to empirical "theory" about human behavior. He had wanted to add to understanding of the American experience. In that sense, he was as much a teacher as a writer. His identity, as the Jungian analyst had seen, was as Hermes, carrying the torch of "good news." But how was he to do that in retirement?

What was he to do? Then he had a bit of luck. An academic friend told him that an excellent midwestern college had hired a mutual friend to teach on a term appointment of five years that could be renewed. The pay was good but not great. He applied for a position and was appointed. His new colleagues were happy to have him. He moved to the small town and attractive campus. He could teach and develop his courses more fully than time had permitted with his research schedule. He loved it.

After he had been there for two years, he went to a cocktail party and was introduced to a woman who told him that she was a full professor who taught anthropology. She was nice looking and they struck up a conversation.

"Perhaps we could have lunch some time," he offered.

"I would enjoy that," she responded with a smile.

Printed in Great Britain
by Amazon